My Very Own® Fairy Tale

This book was made especially for
Zia Gould

Wishing You a Life Full of Happiness!
Vince & Heidi
2013

Written by Maia Haag
Illustrated by Joyce Patti
Book and fairy dress design by Haag Design, Inc.

PERSONALIZED CHILDREN'S BOOKS

Item#: 118528 UPC Code: 898420002021 SKU: BK200 Date Printed: June 21, 2013 Manufacturer ID: 15436A

D1314705

In a magical garden of flowers and berries
there lived a group of beautiful fairies.
They arose and stretched in the morning sun.
A very important day had begun.

The Mulberry Fairy
flew up quite high
and opened her wings
against the sky.

"Wake up, little fairies, so you can hear.
The time for choosing our princess is near.
Please describe the girl you'd like to crown
with a flower tiara and a princess gown.
Who knows a girl who'd be just right?
We'll crown our fairy princess tonight!"

Z

"I know a Zestful girl who spends each day
enjoying her life in a jubilant way."

Zinnia Fairy

Zi

I

"I have an Intelligent friend
who's as bright as a star.
She will flourish like Ivy,
and she'll go very far."

Ivy Fairy

Zia

The Azalea Fairy
splashed in the sun.
"I have an Adorable
friend who likes to have fun!"

Azalea Fairy

The fairies swirled gently down through the air
holding ribbons, flowers and berries with care.

As the Mulberry fairy came floating down,
she wondered which girl the fairies should crown.
"Are the letters together giving us clues
about which girl the fairies should choose?"

"Zia is the name that has been revealed!"
she said as she landed with grace on the field.
Her thoughts were starting to spin and whirl.
"Have we all been describing the very same girl?"

The fairies sewed petals and pillows by hand
to make a throne that was elegant and grand.

While the other fairies decorated the throne,
the Mulberry fairy thought all on her own:
"To know for certain which girl is the one,
we need her last name, so we've only begun.
I will ask more fairies which girl they'd choose.
We can see which letters they magically use."

She gathered the fairies and stated out loud,
"We need a princess who'll make us all proud.
Who's the next fairy with something to say
about the special girl we are choosing today?"

*"This very Good girl knows wrong from right.
She has learned her manners and is very polite."*

Gooseberry Fairy

G

"This Open-minded girl
respects everyone's views.
I think she's the girl
the fairies should choose!"

Olive Fairy

Go

"This Unforgettable girl has an aura all her own.
Everyone would notice her up on the throne."

Umbrella Plant Fairy

Gou

"This Lighthearted girl
tells the best jokes you'll hear.
As our princess, she'd make us
all chuckle and cheer!"

Loganberry Fairy

Goul

"This Darling girl will bring us more smiles
than fields of daisies that go on for miles."

Daisy Fairy

Gould

The Mulberry Fairy flew up high to say,
"We've chosen a wonderful girl today!"

"Zia Gould, we think that you're great.
The time has come. We can no longer wait.
Please sit upon this magnificent throne.
It's made of petals that we have hand-sewn."

"We crown you now with ribbons and berries
and name you the princess of all the fairies!"

The Fairy Patch

For extra fun, go back and look for hidden fairies throughout your book. Some of us can be very small. Search each page to find us all!

Angel's Trumpet

Some angel's trumpet flowers can be up to one foot long! They're a great hiding place when I play hide-and-seek with other fairies.

Apple Blossom

Did you know that bees are needed to make apples? Bees carry pollen between apple blossoms, and then the flowers produce apples.

Aster

Aster comes from the Greek word for "star." Some aster blooms look like stars, and others look like soft fluffy powder puffs.

Azalea (a-ZAEL-ya)

Butterflies and hummingbirds love these bright flowers as much as I do! Azaleas are flowering shrubs from Asia and America.

Blueberry

Have you heard that blueberries can help you remember things? I call them "brain berries," and I eat them every morning.

Boysenberry

Boysenberries are a cross between blackberries, raspberries and loganberries. These big, juicy berries make my fingers turn purple.

Cranberry

Did you know that growers harvest cranberries by flooding the field (called a "bog") with water? The cranberries float to the surface!

Currant

Currant berries are red, very round and full of vitamins. I like to pretend that they look like balloons, carrying me high in the sky.

Daisy

American colonists treated cuts and bruises with a daisy lotion. I like to use these flowers to make pretty daisy-chain necklaces.

Dewberry

Dewberries look like little, black raspberries growing along the ground. I have to fly way down low to pick them.

Emilia (e-MIL-ya)

The emilia flower is also called the tassle flower because of its shape. Do you like the flapper dress that I made out of them?

English Daisy

The name *daisy* comes from "Day's Eye" because the daisy flower opens up its petals to "see" during the day, and it closes at night.

English Lavender
Lavender flowers have a wonderful smell, and they're used in soaps and shampoos. I made my own English Lavender perfume.

Huckleberry
Eating huckleberries can help you see better. Since I eat huckleberries all the time, I can see little fairies from over a mile away.

Evening Primrose
Do you know how this flower got its name? The blooms open in the evening, and they close by noon the following day.

Inula (IN-yew-luh)
The Chinese used to dry Inula flowers, bake them with honey, and use them as a cough medicine. I prefer to eat honey without petals mixed in!

Fern
Geologists believe that ferns have grown on Earth for at least 400 million years. They've always been a soft bed for fairies.

Iris
Iris is the Greek word for "rainbow," and this flower is available in a wide array of colors. Violet is my favorite color. What's yours?

Foxglove
Scandinavians say that fairies tell foxes to ring foxglove bells to warn other foxes of approaching hunters. Do you think it's true?

Ivy
Ivy is a vine that climbs up trees and buildings. Sometimes ivy can cover a whole tree or even a whole building!

Geranium (je-RAY-nee-um)
Did you know that *geranium* is a Greek word meaning "crane?" That's because the seed pods of a geranium look like a crane's bill.

Ixia
The ixia is from South Africa, and it has colorful, star-shaped petals. Each time I wish upon a star, I pick one of these flowers.

Gooseberry
You can find me eating gooseberries at the edge of meadows. These round berries are popular in Scotland for making pies and jams.

Jostaberry (YUST-a-berry)
I love to swing in jostaberry bushes and taste their tangy-sweet flavor. Jostaberries are a cross between blackcurrants and gooseberries.

Hollyberry
Do you know why the British started bringing holly inside at Christmas? – to let woodland spirits hide in the leaves and get out of the cold!

Juneberry
I make delicious puddings and pies with sweet juneberries. I even made pantaloons one day out of two big juneberries!

Kingfisher Daisy
The leaves of this flower grow like a low carpet in our garden, with bright blue flowers on top. I like to dance across their leaves.

Nepeta (NEP-eta)
I have a pet kitten who rolls around on this plant. Nepeta plants are used to make Catnip, a treat that cats love. It makes cats crazy!

Kokia (Koe-KEE-ah)
This gorgeous red flower from Hawaii is endangered and almost extinct. The flower is 4-5 inches wide, so it's a perfect fairy bed.

New Zealand Flax
This plant's leaves were used by the Maori tribes in New Zealand to weave baskets. I weaved the leaves together to make my long gown.

Lily
Did you know that lily bulbs are boiled, dried and used in a Japanese dish that is eaten at the Japanese New Year? I wonder how it tastes.

Northland
During the summer I pick northland berries, which are a type of blueberry. I save them to eat during my favorite season: winter!

Lingonberry
In Sweden, people like to make meatball sauce out of these small red berries. I like to string lingonberries together to make my own rodeo lasso.

Olive
Can you believe that olive trees live to be over 500 years old? The olive tree in our fairy garden is already 332 years old!

Loganberry
I am a very merry fairy hanging from a loganberry. Can you say that ten times fast? A loganberry is a cross between a blackberry and a raspberry.

Orange Blossom
This white flower blooms on trees that make oranges. All the fairies really like the perfume that I made from its fragrant petals.

Marionberry
These delicious berries are grown in Oregon, and they're great on ice cream. We eat these berries whenever a fairy has a birthday party!

Orchid
Some orchids have a yellow and brown petal that looks like a female bee, and it fools male bees to come over to it!

Mulberry
Mulberry trees can be 70 feet tall. I fly way up high and sit in the shade of mulberry trees to stay cool in the summer.

Pansy
The name *pansy* comes from the French word *pensée*, meaning "thought." That's because the flower looks like a person's face nodding in thought.

Petunia
Butterflies can't get down into this trumpet-shaped flower. Hummingbirds can, so they get all of the nectar. Lucky hummingbirds!

Strawberry
Here's a quiz. What's my favorite dessert? Strawberry shortcake. How many seeds are on the outside of a strawberry? 200 seeds!

Poppy
Have you ever eaten a muffin or bagel with poppy seeds in it? If you have, you've eaten seeds that come from poppy flowers.

Sunflower
Sunflowers can grow to be over 9 feet tall! Native Americans used dried sunflower stalks as building materials as early as 2300 BC.

Queen Anne's Lace
American colonists named this flower Queen Anne's Lace, after the queen of England. Since it looks like lace, I use it to make pretty dresses.

Tayberry
Sweet tayberry jam is one of my favorite foods. Tayberries are a cross between raspberries and blackberries, and they're from Scotland.

Raspberry
Over 57 million pounds of raspberries are harvested in Washington state each year. I guess I'm not the only one who loves raspberries!

Thimbleberry
Thimbleberries look like raspberries, but they're bigger and softer. Thimbleberry plants have no thorns, so I can slide down the leaves for fun.

Rose
Did you know that rose colors have different meanings? Giving red roses means "I Love You," and giving dark pink roses means "Thank You."

Tulip
Tulips are grown in the Netherlands. Tulip bulbs were once used as a kind of money there. Would you want to use tulip bulbs as money?

Rosemary
The leaves of rosemary plants are used to add flavor when cooking. I like to add rosemary leaves to the dishes that I make for the fairies.

Umbrella Plant
I always hide under the umbrella plant's leaves when it rains. The leaves of this plant are a foot wide and look like umbrellas turned inside out.

Slipper Flower
This flower from Mexico and South America got its name because of its pouch-like shape. I really love shoes, so it's my favorite flower.

Ursinia (er-SIN-ee-ah)
These South African flowers are bright and cheery, with a glossy black center and orange daisy petals. I like to call them halloween flowers!

Velvet Flower

Red velvet mandevilla flowers grow on vines that can grow 7-10 feet high in a single season! I like to dive into the water that collects in these flowers.

Xeranthemum (ze-RAN-thah-mum)

This flower's name is so hard to say! The first letter is pronounced as a "Z," not an "X." I dry this flower's petals to make pretty necklaces.

Viola (VIE-oh-lah)

Have you heard that flowers are grouped into families? Violas are smaller than pansies, but they look similar, so they are in the same family.

Yarrow

Yarrow is a flowering plant that has been used on wounds to help with healing. Maybe if my toes get sore from dancing, yarrow could help!

Windflower

Can you guess how the windflower got its name? The wind carries the seeds, so these flowers cover the floor of the woods like a blanket.

Yew

A yew is an evergreen tree with seeds that are surrounded by a red berry-like covering. We use the wood of this tree to make fairy wands.

Wisteria (wis-TEE-rih-ah)

Wisteria flowers grow on a vine. The vine can cover a whole tree or house! The purple flower's shape reminds me of grapes hanging on a vine.

Zinnia (ZIN-ee-ah)

Some people say that the zinnia symbolizes "faraway friends." I would like to give you a zinnia so that we can begin a new friendship.

PERSONALIZED CHILDREN'S BOOKS

www.iseeme.com / *1.877.744.3210 (toll free)*

See all the personalized titles from I See Me! Inc:

My Very Own® Name
My Very Own® Fairy Tale
My Very Own® Pirate Tale
The Super, Incredible Big Brother
The Super, Incredible Big Sister
The World According To Me
Who Loves Me?
God Loves You!
A Christmas Bear for Me
A Hanukkah Bear for Me

14505 27th Avenue North, Plymouth, MN 55447